JAZZ

Progressive saxophone pieces with piano accompaniment

ARRANGED BY STEPHEN DURO

Chester Music
(A division of Music Sales Limited)
8/9 Frith Street
London W1V 5TZ

PREFACE

Here are 11 songs carefully chosen from the repertory of jazz 'standards'. Playing these arrangements calls for particular interpretative skills; here are a few suggestions to help your performance.

Rhythmical numbers should aim to set the foot tapping. In many cases this can be achieved by subtly accentuating the second and fourth beats in a bar. Groups of even quavers ♫♫ should generally be played as if written ♪♪♪♪ - known as 'swung'. On the other hand, songs in slow tempi should be played 'straight' (with even quavers) more often than not. Some of the ballads make use of rich harmonies and all such passages should be unhurried.

The songs are arranged according to difficulty, with the easier pieces (approximately Grade III standard of the Associated Board) appearing first, and the harder ones (Grade V/VI standard) towards the end.

Stephen Duro

Visit the Music Sales Internet Music Shop
at http://www.musicsales.co.uk

This book © Copyright 1997 Chester Music
Order No. CH61309   ISBN 0-7119-6517-X

Music processed by Allegro Reproductions.
Cover design by 4i Limited.
Printed in the United Kingdom by Caligraving Limited, Thetford, Norfolk.

CONTENTS

FLY ME TO THE MOON

Words and music by Bart Howard

Originally written as a waltz, this song has long
been a favourite of jazz instrumentalists.

Moderately

D.S. al Coda

CODA

HERE'S THAT RAINY DAY

Words by Johnny Burke and music by
Jimmy Van Heusen

To be played gently throughout. The tune should
be slightly accentuated and should feel unhurried.

Not too slow

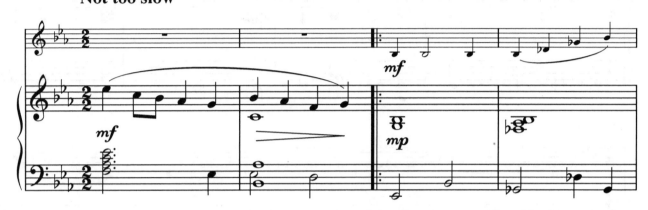

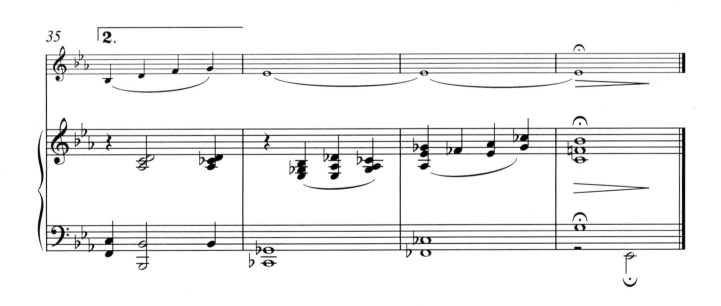

MANHATTAN SPIRITUAL

By Billy Maxted

A piece which is reminiscent of those hand clapping gospel songs. The performers should try to evoke a happy yet fervent atmosphere.

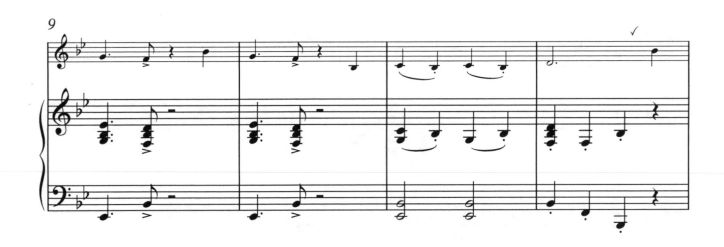

LI'L DARLIN'

Words by Bart Howard and music by Neal Hefti

This piece demands a totally relaxed style of playing, whilst keeping the semblance of a beat going. The quaver passages beginning at bar 10 should have a $\frac{12}{8}$ feel.

Slow

TAKE THE 'A' TRAIN

Words and music by Billy Strayhorn

A piece made famous by the Duke Ellington Orchestra. The tune needs to be stated boldly with strong accents on the fourth and eighth quavers.

Medium swing

19

I'LL REMEMBER APRIL

Words and music by Don Raye, Gene de Paul and Patricia Johnson

The long melodic lines in this classic ballad will benefit from being played in a gentle, unhurried manner. The dynamic range need never rise above a *mezzo forte*.

Not too fast

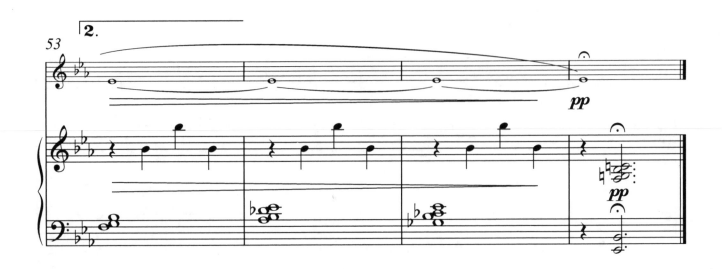

CHELSEA BRIDGE

By Billy Strayhorn

The composer of this haunting ballad was for many years an associate of the legendary Duke Ellington. The arrangement requires quiet, atmospheric playing.

Moderately slow

I'M BEGINNING TO SEE THE LIGHT

Words and music by Harry James, Duke Ellington,
Johnny Hodges and Don George

It is effective if the pianist establishes a crisp left
hand rhythm, crotchet followed by semiquaver,
in the opening 4 bars. In stating the theme the
soloist should play with a $\frac{12}{8}$ feel.

Moderately

BERNIE'S TUNE

By Bernie Miller

This is a classic of the 'cool' repertoire. A feature of the 'cool' style of playing is that the music should have a feeling of restraint and power held in reserve.

Moderately

LULLABY OF BIRDLAND

Words by George David Weiss and
music by George Shearing

This tune combines both even quavers, as in bars 7 and 11, and 'swung' quavers, i.e. notes with a $\frac{12}{8}$ feel. The arrangement should sound smooth and relaxed throughout.

Medium swing

D.S. al Coda

CARAVAN

By Duke Ellington, Irving Mills and Juan Tizol

The tempo indication can be modified to 'not too fast' at the discretion of the performer.

Moderately fast

Also in this series...

The complete series of progressive piano solos, graded from Associated Board grades III to V. Each piece is arranged and fingered in authentic style and includes helpful playing and style notes, fingering and chord symbols.

JUST BLUES
Basin Street Blues, Angel Eyes,
The Lady Sings The Blues
...and many more.
CH61056

JUST JAZZ
Caravan, Fascinating Rhythm,
Lullaby of Birdland
...and many more.
CH61057

JUST LATIN
The Girl From Ipanema,
One Note Samba, Desafinado
...and many more.
CH61217

JUST ROCK
Wonderwall, All Shook Up,
Can't Buy Me Love
...and many more.
CH61218

JUST POP
Unchained Melody, Fernando,
Every Breath You Take, Hey Jude
...and many more.
CH61280

JUST SWING
Honeysuckle Rose,
Sophisticated Lady, Come Fly With Me
...and many more.
CH61281

JUST RAGS
The Entertainer, Maple Leaf Rag,
Black And White Rag
...and many more.
CH61282

Also in this series:
JUST JAZZ for alto saxophone and piano accompaniment
JUST BLUES for alto saxophone and piano accompaniment

Chester Music Limited
Exclusive distributors:
Music Sales Limited, Newmarket Road,
Bury St Edmunds, Suffolk IP33 3YB.